WHEN THEIR BODIES LEAVE THEM

Words by Cecilia Vinkel and Oshri Liron Hakak

Art by Andrea Ceballos García

BUTTERFLYON BOOKS

When Their Bodies Leave Them
Written by Oshri Liron Hakak and Cecilia Vinkel, illustrated by Andrea Ceballos García

Published by Butterflyon Books
Los Angeles
ISBN 978-1-7349790-9-1

Noga   Richard R.   Ama tualo   Alok Modi Tiaga

Maryam Shabazz   .لبقتسملاو رضاحلاو يضاملا في نيرخآلاب نوطبترم نحن   אנחנו תמיד קשורים   Kian Richard L.

Amitai Gidi   Mathilde Xavi Jacob Makak   itakuye oyasin   Albert

Thay   Vladimir Romansky Jacob Charles Lavi   Mark

          Abhinav Kapur   Raymundo and Anita Ang Esther

     Hanna Frida Møller   Daniel   Birgit Rita Møller   우리는 항상 연결 되어 있다.

        Johannes Vinkel   Ole Christian Møller   Jonathan Dowdle

      Juana Maria d'Artnelly Althaus Vinkel   Mama Sally Agami

Somehow we are always united

Dedicated to all the beautiful souls who have
Andrew crossed the threshold of the rainbow, Mark
and dedicated to all the people with loved
Steven ones whose bodies have left them. Sadiq
Con amor,   A little boy with no name

Oshri, Andrea & Cecilia

Pa Fofanah

       Theis Mattsson   Nagi and Aziza Harkham   David S

Manolo   To my grandparents Rafael, Gloria and Belén   Dell

         To my friend brother Manolo and his father

Eli Chammou   Hal Herman

          To My Grandfather Enrique   Patrick H

To my uncle Enrique
De alguna manera siempre estamos unidos   Tali Ruber
To my beloved dog Pancha
                Miriam and Carl Reitzenstein

Мы всё связаны

På en måde er vi altid forbundet

When their bodies leave them,
they're still here.

1

Still, it's good to weep
and to shed our tears...

3

Crying is like dedicating a fountain
to a beloved who has died;
a fountain made out
of the flesh of our eyes.

When that fountain overflows,
by and by, our beloved's spirit
can sail forth on a boat guided
by the winds of our sighs.

A river of our tears carries
them lovingly on.
As the tears dry, their boat glides into
a mysterious, unseen space...
and they are not gone.

Our heart is bound to their spirit
with an unbreakable rope.
In our quiet or in our cries,
we may feel a tug from the beloved,
a tug that tells us to hope,
to love and to live!
A tug that soothes us even as we mope.

11

In the spacious, earthy
land of our dreaming,
we may also see our
beloved beaming.

They may suggest that now
they're better off...
After all, now they've managed
to get rid of that cough.

15

They might tell us that
from their body they are free,
and yet even without eyes,
they still see.

17

In fact,
they see even more clearly than ever,
in a way so wise they can predict
or even pose as the weather!

*We see beyond time
and through space. We see it all.
We see the alwaysness, we see it all.*

They might go on to explain…

When our bodies leave us,
we don't have mouths or tongues to talk,
yet we speak in, as,
and through everything...

We are the butterflies butter-flapping,
the little birds bird-singing,
and every little whisper
of the whirls in the wind.

Try to listen as we tell you thank you,
try to listen as we tell you we love you…
we will listen, too, for you.

27

When our bodies leave us,
we don't have any ears…
and by now, you may have guessed —
we hear quite well!

29

In the world we're in,
your quietest prayers we hear
as if you're singing out
through a loudspeaker, Dear.
We're helping you blossom,
you needn't fear.

When our bodies leave us,
we don't have arms to hug you,
yet we do it all the time.
The subtle sense of a steady hand of care
on your shoulder,
or of a tear brushed gently
from your cheek.

33

That no-reason joy,
that universal tickle you feel
is our hug,
and we do it with every particle of Love
in this universe.

When our bodies leave us,
we don't have any legs
or any feet to move around...
which is why you can bring us to you,
to embrace you,
at the speedy speed of thought.

Your beloved might go on and on
to share how their world is
once we lose them here,
and remind us of our interwoven care.

In our dreams and quiet
we can still chat together.
And though one is in a body
and one is not,
they can still share lessons
to be taught.

During times of torment
and tornadoes,
in the worst of life's weather,
We might call on their aid
so they can send us a tether.

So when their bodies leave them,
it's okay to shout,
and it's okay to cry,
and it's okay to feel
confused and surprised.

45

It's okay to miss them,
and it's possible to kiss them,
and it's loving for peace of spirit
to wish for them.
It's okay to hold them,
and even to scold them.
After all... it's okay to feel sad or mad
we can no longer behold them...
not in exactly the same way, at least.

In our earthly bodies we live on
and they continue within
and around us,
to help comfort, restore,
and ground us.

How should this book finish
when a person does not?

We can try to figure it out,
but perhaps... we cannot.

Instead let's take in a breath of life
and our love will fly
to the beloved who's nearby.
As we let the breath go,
our love soars to where they roam,
behind the scenes of
this part of the show.

THE BEND

Resources

Below we have listed a few resources and organizations committed to helping you in your grieving process.

General Grief Resources:

Gary Roe
garyroe.com

David Kessler
grief.com

Christina Rasmussen
christinarasmussen.com

For families who have lost children:

The Compassionate Friends (International)
www.compassionatefriends.org/

The Miss Foundation (US)
www.missfoundation.org

You can also visit the Selah Carefarm (US)
https://www.missfoundation.org/selah-carefarm/

Local Organizations (Los Angeles):

Our House Grief Support Center
ourhouse-grief.org

WeSPARK
wespark.org

Didi Hirsch
didihirsch.org

Keep in Touch

You can find the creators of this book on Instagram -

Andrea Ceballos García at @andreakushisha
Cecilia Vinkel at @ceciliavinkel
Oshri Hakak at @oshrihakak

More titles by Butterflyon Books:

ButterflyonBooks.com

Books for Grown-Ups:

Children's Books:

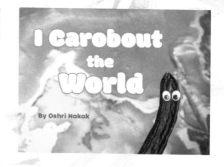

Draw-Wings

Happy Minutes
a book about making the best of our minutes

CPSIA information can be obtained
at www.ICGtesting.com
Printed in the USA
BVHW012208300623
666615BV00002B/34